A Primary Teacher's Handbook Science

Suzanne Kirk

Acknowledgements

Folens books are protected by international copyright laws. All rights are reserved. The copyright of all materials in this book, except where otherwise stated, remains the property of the publisher and author. No part of this publication may be reproduced, stored in a retrieval system, or transmitted, in any form or by any means, for whatever purpose, without the written permission of Folens Limited.

Suzanne Kirk hereby asserts her moral right to be identified as the author of this work in accordance with the Copyright, Designs and Patents Act 1988.

With thanks to:
Dr Katherine Kirk, Glasgow University; Henry Clarke, Science coordinator, and staff and pupils of Holly Hill Primary School, Selston, Nottinghamshire; Underwood C of E Primary School, Underwood, Nottinghamshire; Kirkstead Junior School, Pinxton, Derbyshire; Tranmoor Primary School, Doncaster; Leedon Lower School, Leighton Buzzard, Bedfordshire.

Photographs:
Kelvin Freeman
Except:
P30: Suzanne Kirk
P51: Steve Harrison
P63: Professor Alexander Fleming (1881-1955) Science Museum/Science and Society Picture Library.

Material from the National Curriculum is Crown copyright and is reproduced with the permission of the Controller of HMSO.

Editor: Hayley Willer   Design: Andy Bailey   Layout artist: Suzanne Ward
Cover image: Zubair Haveliwala (space picture), Uplands Junior School, Leicestershire; Munassir Rasool (Science title), Uplands Junior School, Leicestershire
Cover design: Andy Bailey/Alison Colver

© 1998 Folens Limited, on behalf of the author.

Every effort has been made to contact copyright holders of material used in this book. If any have been overlooked, we will be pleased to make any necessary arrangements.

First published 1998 by Folens Limited, Dunstable and Dublin.
Folens Limited, Albert House, Apex Business Centre, Boscombe Road, Dunstable, LU5 4RL, England.

ISBN 1 85276281-0

Printed in Singapore by Craft Print.

Contents

Introduction and aims

Every child has the right to experience science – its fascinations, pleasures and complexities. Science has shaped our past, influences whatever we do in our lives and will play a major role in the future of our planet and its inhabitants.

Science is firmly established as a vital part of the School Curriculum. The National Curriculum for Science provides a basic statutory framework to be used in planning and assessing at Key Stages 1 and 2. The Programmes of Study set out what is to be taught and the Attainment Targets indicate the expected standards of pupils' performance. Level Descriptions help teachers to describe the types and range of performance that individual pupils, working at a particular level, should characteristically demonstrate during their Primary Science education.

Identifying shells.

Aims of the handbook

To support the teaching of Science at Key Stages 1 and 2 by:

- ☞ encouraging good practice in Science education
- ☞ boosting teacher confidence and creating enthusiasm for this core subject
- ☞ assisting with policy writing and planning
- ☞ ensuring effective delivery of the Programmes of Study of the National Curriculum
- ☞ emphasising the importance of first-hand experience and challenging investigative work
- ☞ outlining the development of science skills
- ☞ demonstrating links with cross-curricular areas and other subject areas
- ☞ showing how display can be effective and resources managed efficiently
- ☞ highlighting safety measures and reducing risks
- ☞ ensuring that every child, regardless of ability, gender, race or physical disability, receives equal opportunities from the teaching of Science.

Why teach Science?

To develop children's understanding

- ☞ To fulfil the requirements of Science as a core subject of the National Curriculum.

- ☞ To introduce children to the many aspects of scientific knowledge and experience.

- ☞ To help children gain an insight into the history of science and to realise that today's achievements are a culmination of previous scientific developments.

- ☞ To appreciate the work of past and present scientists.

- ☞ To show where science is carried out day by day, and the range of people involved.

- ☞ To help children make decisions concerning environmental, moral and social issues.

To encourage children's skills

- ☞ To develop the scientific skills of investigation.

- ☞ To provide opportunities for using knowledge and practising acquired skills.

- ☞ To provide opportunities for checking everyday ideas.

- ☞ To encourage cooperation, collaboration and the sharing of ideas.

- ☞ To provide opportunities for children to communicate.

- ☞ To give confidence and to encourage initiative and creativity.

To develop children's attitudes

- ☞ To extend children's natural curiosity and wonder about the world in which they are growing.

- ☞ To develop enthusiasm for an area of the Curriculum that affects every part of our lives.

- ☞ To encourage children to look after themselves and be aware of dangers and safety procedures.

- ☞ To prepare children to lead a healthy and responsible adult life.

- ☞ To initiate a lifelong interest in the natural world.

- ☞ To inspire the scientists of the future.

Writing a policy statement

To teach Science effectively and deliver the National Curriculum successfully, every school needs to produce a whole-school policy statement and scheme of work for Science. The purpose of this is to:

- state how the National Curriculum statutory orders will be met
- outline the agreed approaches and methods to be used in teaching Science
- demonstrate the school's commitment to Science
- give teachers confidence and provide parents, governors and OFSTED with a clear overview of Science provision within the school.

Producing a school policy and scheme of work for Science is usually the responsibility of the curriculum coordinator, but in collaboration with the whole staff. It is a continuous cyclic process of development. However, it is the gradual development of the policy that will be of greater value to individual teachers than the completed document itself.

Before beginning or reviewing a policy an audit will need to be carried out.

Where are we now?
Audit: Review existing policies and targets, documentation, current practice, equipment, resources and time allocation to highlight areas of strength and weakness.

Where do we want to be?
To have a working policy and a well-organised but flexible scheme of work that acknowledges the need for continuity, progression, breadth and balance.

How will we know when we have arrived?
Policy successfully in place with regular in-built systems to monitor and evaluate achievements and targets set. Parents and governors informed of practice, procedures and expectations.

How do we get there?
Whole-staff collaboration in prioritising, target setting and decision making. Identification of (staff) training needs, use of external support (e.g. advisory service), planned financial allocation.

Key elements of a Science policy statement

When writing a policy, it should be possible to devise a framework that is common to all areas of the Curriculum, but flexible enough to accommodate individual aspects specific to each subject. A common format makes it easier to write policies and helps achieve consistency across the Curriculum.

The following headings may be useful. You might need to refer to the procedures recorded in the whole-school policy statement.

- Why we teach Science
- Aims and objectives
- Content/framework
- Schemes of work
- Teaching and learning styles
- Continuity of teaching
- Progression of learning
- Differentiation
- Assessment
- Recording
- Reporting
- Equal opportunities
- Resources
- Health and safety
- Extra-curricular provision
- Role of coordinator
- Role of head teacher
- Review of policy

Key elements of a policy statement

This page presents the various headings that might be useful for a school policy statement. Ideas and advice for most of these headings can be found throughout this book.

Helpful headings when writing a policy statement

Why we teach Science
☛ The reasons behind the school's commitment to Science teaching, including the importance of science in everyday life, the fascination it holds for children and its status as a core subject of the National Curriculum. (See page 5.)

Aims of Science teaching
☛ Encouraging a positive attitude towards all areas of science; extending a child's experience and natural curiosity to stimulate enquiry and investigation; developing scientific knowledge and skills. (See page 5.)

Objectives
☛ How the aims will be achieved in relation to the minimum requirements of the National Curriculum.

Content
☛ How the National Curriculum is to be organised within the Key Stages; the provision for cross-curricular links and topics to be covered. (See pages 8–9 and 48–49.)

Schemes of work
☛ Details of planning procedures over appropriate Key Stages, long-, medium- and short-term planning: (See pages 8–9.)

Teaching and learning styles
☛ The value of first-hand experience and learning through investigation; the extent to which class, group and individual situations will be used; how individuality in teaching methods will be encouraged; the importance given to role-play, art, music, visits.

Continuity of teaching
☛ How planning between classes, year groups and across Key Stages ensures continuous coverage of the National Curriculum.

Progression of learning
☛ The strategies employed to ensure successful progression through knowledge, understanding and skills. (See pages 23–41.)

Differentiation
☛ How this is integrated into planning. (See page 47.)

Assessment
☛ Procedures that are followed; how continuous and periodic assessment are used to determine appropriate work for each child; arrangements for SATs. (See pages 42–43.)

Recording
☛ Methods employed; procedures followed; progress and achievement monitored.

Reporting
☛ Procedures for reporting to parents, governors, local authority, OFSTED and the child's next school.

Equal opportunities
☛ School's commitment regarding every child's entitlement and encouragement in Science regardless of gender, race and difficulties encountered.

Resources
☛ Materials and equipment, books and videos available, their location and management; children's responsibilities; outdoor and off-site arrangements; procedures for plants and animals in school. (See pages 58–60.)

Health and safety
☛ Teachers' and children's responsibilities; safety codes and manuals that are available for reference.

Extra-curricular provision
☛ Reference to any clubs or workshops incorporating science activities.

Role of coordinator
☛ Who this is and their responsibilities, including planning, monitoring, supporting colleagues, organising resources, arranging INSET and keeping up to date with developments.

Role of head teacher
☛ Encouraging staff to teach Science effectively and ensuring the policy is implemented and reviewed, monitored and evaluated.

Review of policy
☛ Date and procedure.

Writing a scheme of work

Develop a model appropriate to the school, taking into account:
- ☞ number of children
- ☞ arrangement of classes
- ☞ school calendar
- ☞ seasons.

Long-term planning:
- ☞ how the Science Curriculum is to be organised over Key Stage 1 and Key Stage 2.

Medium-term planning:
- ☞ termly or half-termly units of study.

Short-term planning:
- ☞ weekly or fortnightly proposals.

A scheme of work should:
- ☞ be easy to use
- ☞ relate to the Science Curriculum
- ☞ reflect the school Science policy
- ☞ provide an overview of Science within the school
- ☞ give teachers confidence to teach Science
- ☞ ensure continuity of content coverage
- ☞ facilitate progression of learning
- ☞ enable effective assessment to take place
- ☞ assist with monitoring
- ☞ allow room for flexibility.

Using the Programmes of Study and Level Descriptions as a guide:
- ☞ map out the teaching of Science
- ☞ locate areas of study, topics, themes and units

Planning

Planning should provide:
- ☞ a set of activities and investigations, including assessment tasks
- ☞ details of resources required
- ☞ an indication of the arrangement of classes
- ☞ arrangements for differentiation, including extension
- ☞ ideas for display
- ☞ provision for equality of access.

Key Stage 1
Each area of the Programme of Study can be experienced once
with:
- one complete investigation each term

and:
- ongoing experiences of growing plants, caring for animals, seasonal observations and weather recording.

Key Stage 2
The Programme of Study could be organised **either** as:
- two cycles; each area experienced (twice) on two levels of understanding

or:
- over four years; each area of content assigned a specific slot with careful consideration of progression

with:
- one complete investigation each term

and:
- revision time planned into Year 6 (optional).

Managing time

Planning science activities involves careful consideration regarding time. Often it is important that an investigation is completed within a session and without interruptions. It can be vital to an investigation that observations and measurements are continued and data collected. Some tests need longer to complete and are best arranged to start at the beginning of a day or week. Lunchtimes, weekends and holidays need to be taken into account. Some activities are more appropriate at certain times of the year – growing plants and incubating eggs are more successful during the second half of the spring term and the summer term.

Advantage should be taken of the seasons when children are studying plant- and animal-life or temperatures.

Planning should be flexible enough to include topical and local issues that arise – events such as 'Science and Technology Week', 'Environment Day', and purposeful competitions.

- ☞ decide when, and the number of times, each area of the Curriculum will be experienced by a child
- ☞ highlight links with other subjects
- ☞ integrate cross-curricular themes
- ☞ demonstrate progression across and between Key Stages.

A scheme of work

A successful scheme of work is appropriate to the needs of a school. When devising an individual scheme of work you will need to consider:

☞ progression of knowledge, concepts and skills

☞ the arrangement of the classes in relation to the year groupings of the children

☞ skills of individual teachers

☞ use of resources, visits and expertise

☞ cross-curricular links

☞ seasonal issues and the school's calendar

☞ SATs and any time allowed for revision.

A well-planned scheme of work will also indicate when:

☞ each area of the Curriculum is to be taught

☞ there is opportunity for an investigation

☞ assessment is appropriate.

At Key Stage 1, the content of the Programmes of Study for Life Processes and Living Things, Materials and their Properties and Physical Processes can be organised into six modules to be taught over two years. (See following table.)

	Term 1	Term 2	Term 3
Year 1	**Ourselves**	**Light and sound**	**Living things in their environment**
	Life Processes and Living Things (1b, 2a, b, c, d, e, f, 4a)	Physical Processes (3a, b, c, d, e)	Life Processes and Living Things (1a, 4b, 5a, b)
Year 2	**Electricity, forces and motion**	**Materials**	**Plants**
	Physical Processes (1a, b, c, 2a, b, c, d)	Materials and their Properties (1a, b, c, d, e, 2a, b)	Life Processes and Living Things (1a, 3a, b, c, 4b)

Below is an example of how the content of Life Processes and Living Things, Materials and their Properties and Physical Processes could be organised over the four-year cycle of Key Stage 2. Although points of reference are given, there will need to be overlapping as topics are revised, and as the complete picture of each area is created.

	Term 1	Term 2	Term 3
	Life Processes and Living Things	**Materials and their Properties**	**Physical Processes**
Year 3	Humans – nutrition: teeth, diet, growth (other animals) (1a, 2a, b) Plants – growth, roots, seed dispersal (1b, 3a, c, d)	Grouping and classifying everyday materials (1a) Changes – heating and cooling (2a, b, c)	Light and sound (3a, b, c, d, e) The Earth and beyond (4a, b)
Year 4	Humans – movement: skeleton and muscles (other animals) (1a, 2f) Plants – germination (3d) Classification and habitats (4a, 5a, b)	Rocks and soils (1d) Changes (2c, d, f) Sieving and filtering (3a, b, c)	Electricity (1a, b, d) Forces (2a, b, c, f, g)
Year 5	Humans – circulation: heart and exercise (2c, d, e) Plants – food production (1b, 3b) Food chains (5c, d) Micro-organisms (5e)	Thermal insulators and electrical conductors (1b, c) Water cycle (2e) Solutions – dissolving and evaporating (3b, d, e)	Electricity (1c, d) Light and sound (3c, d, f, g)
Year 6	Human growth and reproduction (other animals) (1a, 2g) Drugs (2h) Plants – reproduction (1b, 3d) Classification (4a)	Solids, liquids and gases (1e)	Forces (2d, e, f, g, h) The Earth and beyond (4c, d)

Interpreting the Programmes of Study

Experimental and Investigative Science

A science investigation involves a range of skills that are developed through planning, obtaining evidence and considering evidence. As children gain confidence and independence they should gradually take on all aspects of an investigation.

This and the following page set out details of the requirements for Experimental and Investigative Science at both Key Stages. Pages 12–13 break this information down into charts for easy reference.

Selecting materials for an investigation.

Planning experimental work

Enquiring
An investigation begins with a question that can:
- be decided by the teacher
- arise from a stimulus, such as an object or a process, arranged by the teacher
- arise from a science activity already in progress
- arise from a topical or seasonal issue.

Children's own questions and ideas are valuable in that they imply ownership and increase motivation for the investigation. Safety and limitations need to be discussed.

Predicting
If children can predict or think what might happen, they are more able to plan their investigation efficiently. They will be using available evidence and their previous knowledge and experience to make their predictions.

Making decisions
For an effective investigation, decisions must be made about information to be collected and the equipment and materials to be used.

Devising a fair test
Children need to recognise a fair test, identifying the factor that is to be changed (the variable), and those that must be kept the same (constants). They should decide which measurements and observations to record and prepare a chart to collect their evidence.

Obtaining evidence

Using equipment
Children need to be able to use the relevant equipment accurately if an investigation is to be successful. They will need to follow their plan, working efficiently and safely, and make sure that they carry out a fair test.

Observing and measuring
Accurate observations and measurements are vital to an investigation. Children must be aware of the importance of collecting evidence by making notes and drawings, and accurately recording data on a previously prepared chart.

Collecting evidence might take place over a long period, or need to be obtained very quickly. Repeating observations and measurements when appropriate can eliminate errors and confirm findings.

Using newton-meters to measure weight in air and water.

Considering evidence

Recording
Tables, charts and graphs, as appropriate, are needed to present results clearly.

Interpreting data
Children should be encouraged to value their results and those of others, to make comparisons and to look for patterns or trends.

Drawing conclusions
Collecting and considering data and other evidence can help children to make decisions about their findings and decide whether the evidence supports the predictions made.

Communicating
It is important that children explain to each other and to adults what they have found out from an investigation, using their scientific knowledge and understanding. This can take the form of speaking, writing, drawing, using diagrams and models, role-play, music and artwork. Listening to others is important in consolidating their learning.

At Key Stage 1 and Key Stage 2, questions can be used to guide children through the process of an investigation. Depending on the nature of the investigation and the extent to which the children carry it out, selected questions can be used as headings on planning and recording sheets.

Key Stage 1

Planning experimental work
- What do you want to find out?
- What do you think might happen?
- How will you make sure the test is fair?

Obtaining evidence
- What can you see happening?
- What can you hear?
- What can you feel?
- Can you smell anything?

- What are you going to measure?
- What will you do to help you remember what happened?

Considering evidence
- What happened?
- What is the same/different?
- What do you think this tells us?
- Is this what you thought would happen?
- Why do you think this happened?

Provide a stimulus for observation and discussion

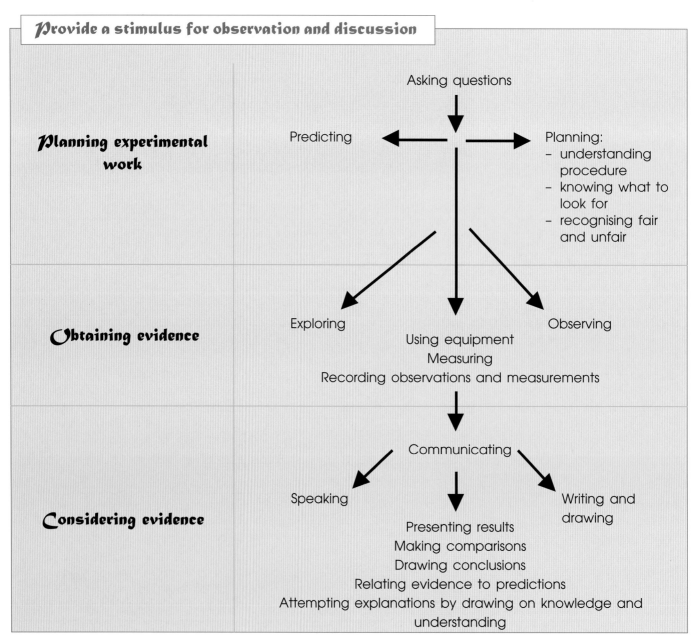

Planning experimental work

Asking questions

Predicting ← → Planning:
- understanding procedure
- knowing what to look for
- recognising fair and unfair

Obtaining evidence

Exploring   Observing

Using equipment
Measuring
Recording observations and measurements

Considering evidence

Communicating

Speaking   Writing and drawing

Presenting results
Making comparisons
Drawing conclusions
Relating evidence to predictions
Attempting explanations by drawing on knowledge and understanding

Key Stage 2

Planning experimental work
- What do you want to find out?
- What do you think might happen?
- What will you be looking for?
- How will you record the evidence collected?
- How will you make sure the test is fair?
- What will you keep the same? What will you change?
- Which materials and equipment will you use?

- How will you make sure the test is safe?
- How long do you expect the test to take?

Obtaining evidence
- How did you carry out the test?
- What can you see happening?
- What did you observe and measure?
- How did you check the observations and measurements?

Considering evidence
- What did you find out?
- How are you presenting your results?
- What do your results show?
- Have you discovered any patterns or trends?
- What conclusions have you come to?
- Is this what you expected?
- Can you explain why this has happened?
- If you did this test again, what would you do differently?

Provide a stimulus for observation and discussion

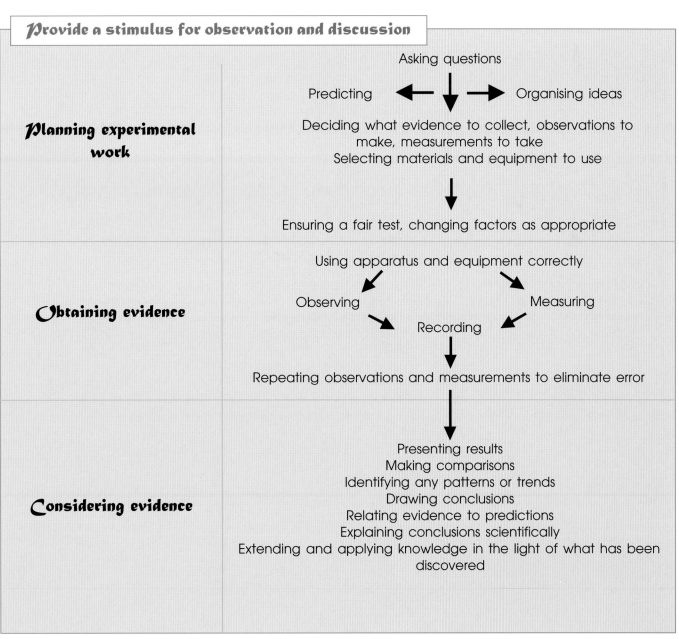

Planning experimental work

Asking questions

Predicting ← ↓ → Organising ideas

Deciding what evidence to collect, observations to make, measurements to take
Selecting materials and equipment to use

↓

Ensuring a fair test, changing factors as appropriate

Obtaining evidence

Using apparatus and equipment correctly

Observing   Measuring

Recording

Repeating observations and measurements to eliminate error

Considering evidence

Presenting results
Making comparisons
Identifying any patterns or trends
Drawing conclusions
Relating evidence to predictions
Explaining conclusions scientifically
Extending and applying knowledge in the light of what has been discovered

Key Stage 1

Programmes of Study
Life Processes and Living Things

1 **Life processes**	**a**	There are differences between things that are living and things that have never been alive; animals and plants are living, other things are not living. Living things breathe, feed, grow, move, reproduce and die.
	b	Animals, including humans, move, feed, grow, use their senses and reproduce. There are different ways of moving, special parts of the body to help with movement and different reasons for moving. Animals eat different foods in different ways and can have special body parts for helping with feeding. Animals use their eyes, ears, noses, mouths and skin to find out about the place where they live. Animals have different ways of reproducing themselves; some parents look after their young, others do not.
2 **Humans as organisms**	**a**	The main external parts of the human body are hands, fingers, thumbs, wrists, arms, elbows, shoulders, neck, head, eyes, ears, nose, mouth, hair, chest, back, legs, knees, ankles, feet, toes, heels.
	b	Humans need food and water to stay alive. Food provides energy to move about, keep warm, think, and make all parts of the body work, grow and repair damage.
	c	To keep the body healthy, humans need to take exercise and eat the right types and the right amounts of food. Exercise keeps the body parts strong, in good working order, and assists growth, as does eating a variety of suitable foods.
	d	Some drugs are useful as medicines. They can be dangerous and must be taken with care and under the supervision of adults.
	e	Humans produce babies that grow into children and then adults.
	f	Humans have senses that they can use to find out about the world around them.

3 **Green plants as organisms**	**a**	Plants need light for healthy growth, and water to prevent them from drying up.
	b	Flowering plants have leaves that make the plants' food and are usually green, flowers that are often brightly coloured and attract insects, stems that support the leaves and flowers and transport water, and roots that hold the plant in the ground and take in water.
	c	Flowering plants grow; the flowers produce seeds that are scattered or collected and when planted and given the right conditions will produce new plants.
4 **Variation and classification**	**a**	Children are the same in many ways; there are also some differences, such as colour of hair, eyes and skin, size and preferences that help us to recognise each other.
	b	Living things can be grouped according to how similar or how different they are, such as whether they have feathers or fur, the number of legs, colour of flower or shape of leaf.

5

Living things in their environment

a There are different kinds of plants and animals in the local environment; plants such as weeds, trees, garden flowers, vegetables, mosses, classroom plants, plants that grow in water; animals, such as minibeasts, birds, domestic and wild mammals and pond-dwelling creatures.

b There are differences between the local environments in which animals choose to live. For example, between garden and woodland, wall and pond, park and street, mown grass and longer grass.

Sorting leaves according to their similarities and differences.

Key Stage 2

Programmes of Study
Life Processes and Living Things

1 **Life processes**	**a**	All animals, as well as humans, feed, move, grow and reproduce. **Feeding:** searching for and obtaining food, types of food, adaptations for feeding, such as beak, teeth, claws. **Growth:** importance of an adequate supply of suitable food, patterns of growth. **Movement:** reasons for moving (e.g. to feed, to reproduce, to escape from enemies, to find shelter); methods, such as swimming, flying, crawling; adaptations, such as flippers, wings, body shape. **Reproduction:** stages of different life cycles for mammals, birds, fish, amphibians, insects; successful reproduction depends on food supply and availability of habitat.
	b	All plants grow, produce food and reproduce.
2 **Humans as organisms**	**a**	Teeth are necessary for biting and chewing; they can decay and need special care.
	b	The human body needs enough food of all types to be active, keep warm, maintain growth, keep healthy.
	c	The heart consists of compartments and valves. It pumps blood around the body.
	d	Blood circulates through a system of arteries and veins, collecting oxygen from the lungs, carrying the oxygen to all parts of the body and returning carbon dioxide to the lungs to be exhaled.
	e	Blood is pumped around the body at different rates, as indicated by a pulse, depending on whether the body is active or at rest.
	f	The skeleton consists of many different bones that support the body. Muscles assist movement.
	g	Humans are born, grow, reach maturity, can reproduce and eventually die.
	h	The human body can be harmed by many substances including tobacco, alcohol and other drugs.

3 **Green plants** **as organisms**	**a**	Light, water and temperature affect the growth of plants; different plants require different variations of these factors.
	b	There is a wide variety of leaves among plants; they need light as an energy source, which they use with carbon dioxide and water to produce food.
	c	The functions of the root are to anchor the plant into the ground and take water and nutrients from the soil for transporting to all parts of the plant.
	d	Flowering plants produce seeds. Flowers are structured to enable pollination by animals or wind. Pollination leads to fertilisation and seed production. There is a wide variety of seeds and methods of seed dispersal. Seeds carry on the information about a plant; they contain a food supply and need the right conditions for germination.
4 **Variation and** **classification**	**a**	There is a wide variety of animals and plants in any locality; they can be grouped according to how similar they are, and identified using keys.
5 **Living things in** **their environment**	**a**	There is a wide range of habitats; each must provide the particular needs of a plant or animal, including shelter, food and climatic conditions.
	b	Animals and plants living in different habitats show differences in structure and habits. These differences suit their environment.
	c	All animals and plants are part of a food chain; they depend on each other and play an important part in the balance of their ecosystem.
	d	The basis of a food chain is that green plants are producers and animals are consumers. Energy is transferred along a food chain.
	e	Micro-organisms are all around us in the air and water, and we can observe their effects; some are beneficial and help with the breakdown of waste, others are harmful and can cause disease.

Examining the roots of plants.

Key Stage 1

Programmes of Study
Materials and their Properties

1 **Grouping materials**	**a**	By exploring and observing safe familiar materials, their similarities and differences can be discovered.
	b	Materials can be grouped according to their appearance; whether they are hard or soft, rough or smooth, heavy or light, firm or bendy, magnetic or non-magnetic, transparent or not.
	c	There are differences between wood, metal, plastic, fabric, paper, glass and rock; some of these materials are natural, others are made by humans.
	d	Many materials have a variety of uses: glass for windows, bottles and decorative purposes; metal for cars, pans, jewellery and machines; wood for buildings, pencils and chairs; plastic for toys, bowls and tables.
	e	Materials are chosen for their specific uses because of their properties: glass is transparent, useful for windows; metal is strong, important for machinery; plastic is lightweight, ideal for buckets; wool is warm and soft, useful for clothing.
2 **Changing materials**	**a**	The shape of objects made from some materials, such as paper, sponge, modelling clay, fabric, thin metal and plastic, can be changed by squashing, bending, twisting and stretching.
	b	Some everyday materials, such as water, chocolate, bread and clay, can be changed by heating or cooling.

Investigating the effects of heating and cooling a range of food types.

Key Stage 2

Programmes of Study
Materials and their Properties

1 **Grouping and classifying materials**	**a**	We use a variety of materials, such as wood, rock, metal, paper, plastic, glass and fabric. There are different types of these materials with properties such as hardness, strength, flexibility, magnetic behaviour, durability and reaction to water, that determine how we use them. Some materials are natural, some are made by humans.
	b	Some materials are used to slow down the transfer of heat.
	c	Electricity can pass easily through some materials, which can be used as conductors; those that electricity cannot pass through are useful as insulators.
	d	Rocks and soils have different characteristics; they vary in appearance, texture, hardness, the rate at which water will pass through them and the ways in which we use them.
	e	Solids, liquids and gases are different in the way that they move and keep their shape and their volume, and therefore in how we use and control them.
2 **Changing materials**	**a**	When materials are mixed, changes can occur.
	b	Heating or cooling materials can cause changes. Temperature is a measure of how hot or cold things are; a thermometer is used to measure temperatures accurately.
	c	Some changes can be reversed, some cannot.
	d	Dissolving, melting, boiling, condensing, freezing and evaporating are all changes that can be reversed.
	e	Evaporation and condensation are natural processes in the water cycle.
	f	Changes that occur when materials, such as wood, wax or natural gas are burned, cannot be reversed.
3 **Separating mixtures of materials**	**a**	When a mixture has solid particles of different sizes, they can be separated by sieving.
	b	Solids that dissolve in water (or any other liquid), make solutions; those that do not dissolve, make mixtures.
	c	Solids that do not dissolve can be separated by filtering.
	d	A dissolved solid can be recovered by evaporating the liquid in which it has dissolved.
	e	There is a limit to how much of a solid will dissolve in an amount of water. This limit is different for different solids.

Key Stage 1

Programmes of Study
Physical Processes

1 Electricity	a	Many everyday appliances use electricity; they can be found in the home, school, office, shop and factory.
	b	Simple circuits can be made using batteries, wires, bulbs and buzzers.
	c	Electrical devices will not work if there is a break in the circuit.
2 Forces and motion	a	When things, such as cars, people, balls and paper planes are moving, they can speed up, slow down or change direction.
	b	Pushes and pulls are forces; pushing opens a door, moves a trolley, operates a switch; pulling moves a toy, lifts a bag, opens a drawer.
	c	Forces can make things speed up, slow down or change direction, such as kicking a football, catching a ball or bouncing a ball.
	d	Forces can change the shapes of objects as in stretching an elastic band, squeezing modelling clay or bouncing a sponge ball.
3 Light and sound	a	Light comes from a variety of sources including the Sun, a bulb, a flame.
	b	Darkness is the absence of light.
	c	There are many kinds of sound and many sources of sound.
	d	Sounds travel away from their sources, getting fainter as they do so.
	e	We hear sounds when they enter our ears.

Key Stage 2

1 Electricity

a A complete circuit, which includes a battery or other power supply, is needed to make electrical devices work.

b Switches are useful for controlling electrical devices.

c A current in a circuit can be varied in different ways to make a bulb brighter or dimmer.

Drawing an electrical circuit.

d Series circuits can be represented by drawings and diagrams; series circuits can be constructed from the information given in drawings and diagrams.

2 Forces and motion

a There are forces of attraction and repulsion between magnets, and forces of attraction between magnets and magnetic materials.

b The Earth attracts all smaller objects with a force known as gravity; this force of attraction gives objects their weight.

c The force of friction, which includes air resistance, slows down moving objects.

d When springs and elastic bands are stretched they exert a force on whatever is stretching them.

e When springs are compressed they exert a force on whatever is compressing them.

f Forces act in particular directions.

g When the forces acting on an object are balanced, the object does not move – a book on a table, a piece of wood floating.

h Unbalanced forces cause things to move; things can speed up, slow down or change direction.

Key Stage

2

Exploring light and reflection.

3 *Light and sound*	**a**	Light travels from a source that could be the Sun, a bulb, or a flame.
	b	There are some materials that light cannot pass through and this causes shadows.
	c	Light is easily reflected from some surfaces, such as mirrors, polished metals and water.
	d	We see light sources because the light from them enters our eyes.
	e	Sounds are made when objects vibrate, such as the strings on musical instruments. However, the vibrations are not always visible.
	f	The pitch and loudness of sounds produced by some vibrating objects, such as a drum or plucked string, can be changed.
	g	Vibrations from sound sources can travel to the ear through a variety of materials, including metal, wood, glass, air and water.
4 *The Earth and beyond*	**a**	The Sun, Earth and Moon are approximately spherical.
	b	The position of the Sun appears to change during the day and shadows change as this happens.
	c	The Earth spins around its own axis; the part of the Earth facing the Sun receives light and the part away from the Sun remains dark.
	d	The Earth orbits the Sun once each year. The Moon takes approximately 28 days to orbit the Earth.

Progression in Experimental and Investigative Science

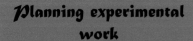

Planning experimental work

Observes and talks.

Asks questions.

Sorts and groups.

Responds to suggestions.

With help, begins to make suggestions that could be turned into investigations.

Can say what might happen without giving reasons.

Nursery/Reception

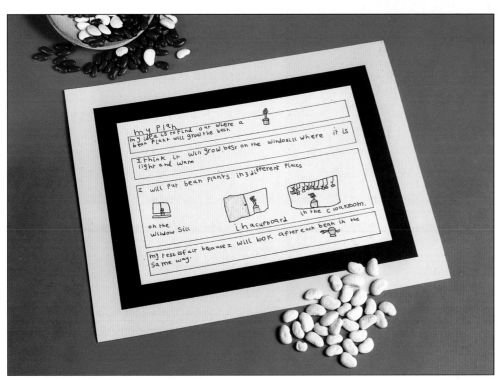

A plan for a plant growth investigation.

Asks questions that can be investigated.

Makes predictions based on everyday evidence.

Initiates and plans an investigation, making predictions based on scientific knowledge and understanding.

Organises ideas and decides on evidence to collect, equipment to use and safety procedures.

Identifies key factors in the investigation.

Recognises when a test is fair.

Asks questions and makes predictions based on relevant knowledge.

Decides what evidence to collect.

Selects suitable equipment.

Recognises the need for a fair test, planning to change one factor while keeping the others the same.

Year 6

Obtaining evidence

Nursery/Reception

Uses all senses to observe plants, animals, materials and processes.

Looks for similarities and differences.

Does simple recording using drawings.

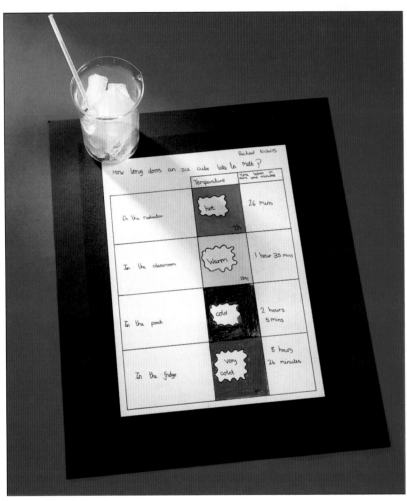

A recording of how long it takes an ice cube to melt at different temperatures.

Makes observations relating to questions or ideas being investigated.

Uses simple equipment.

Records observations orally, in drawings, words or simple tables.

Makes and records relevant observations.

Uses a variety of measuring equipment to support observations.

With help, carries out a fair test.

Uses equipment and materials correctly.

Carries out a fair test and controls variables.

Observes and measures adequately for the investigation.

Collects and records evidence as appropriate.

Carries out a fair test independently, handling a range of variables.

Uses apparatus and equipment accurately.

Makes precise observations and measurements.

Records observations and measurements systematically.

Repeats observations and measurements as necessary.

Year 6

Considering evidence

Nursery/Reception

Answers simple questions relating to observations.

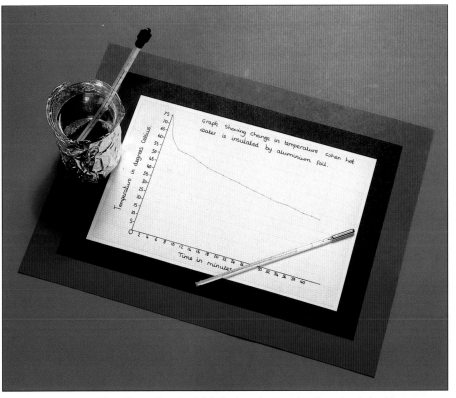

A line graph recording the rate at which hot water cools when insulated by aluminium foil.

Talks about what has happened.

Considers if it was what was expected.

Draws conclusions from observations.

Presents observations for others as drawings or using simple written methods.

Explains the fairness of a test.

Provides explanations for observations and patterns in measurements.

Uses a range of methods to report and present findings.

Presents observations and measurements clearly.

Uses results to construct tables and bar charts when appropriate.

Interprets patterns or trends in data, linking these to the original question, prediction or idea.

Draws conclusions based on observations and measurements.

Relates conclusions to scientific knowledge and understanding.

Plots points on a line graph, using evidence collected.

Interprets information provided by tables, bar charts and line graphs.

Offers explanations for differences in data.

Draws conclusions consistent with evidence.

Explains conclusions in respect of scientific knowledge and understanding.

Evaluates investigations.

Year 6

Progression in Life Processes and Living Things

Recognises that living things grow and die.

Understands that plants and animals are living things.

Is aware that some things are living, others are not living.

Life processes

Nursery/Reception

Begins to understand that animals, including themselves, need to move and must feed in order to grow and survive.

Understands that all animals reproduce themselves.

Learning about living things through caring for a pet rabbit.

Explores the environment, using all senses and recognises the importance of sight, smell, hearing, taste and touch in other animals.

Begins to appreciate the different feeding methods among animals.

Knows that most plants produce their own food.

Understands that plants and animals complete their life cycles by growing and reproducing.

Year 6

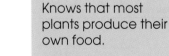

Is aware of differences in the ways animals move, and the reasons why they need to move.

Observes that all plants grow.

Humans as organisms

Nursery/Reception

Identifies and names different parts of the body, and is aware of their functions.

Understands that humans need food and water to stay alive.

Exploration of human joints.

Recognises self as part of the human life cycle.

Begins to use all senses to gain a wider knowledge and understanding of the environment.

Understands that food and exercise play a part in keeping a body healthy.

Knows that using drugs as medicines can be necessary during illness but they need to be used with care and supervision.

Becomes aware of the importance of keeping safe and healthy.

Is aware of the structure and function of the heart and how the blood circulates around the body.

Investigates the effects of exercise and rest on the body.

Is aware of the harmful effects of drugs on the body.

Understands the main stages of the human life cycle.

Is aware of the physical changes that occur during puberty.

Becomes increasingly aware of the workings of the human body and the responsibility of following a healthy lifestyle.

Understands the functions of the teeth and the importance of dental care.

Knows that food is needed for activity and growth, and knows which foods are required for a healthy lifestyle.

Understands the role of the skeleton and muscles in supporting the body and enabling it to move.

Year 6

Green plants as organisms

Nursery/Reception

→

Realises that plants are living things.

Recognises the leaf, flower, stem and root of a flowering plant.

→

Observes that plants need water and light to grow.

Discovers that seeds grow into new plants.

Planting bulbs to investigate growing conditions.

Begins to piece together the life cycle of a flowering plant.

Is aware of the effects of light and water upon plant growth.

Identifies different methods of seed dispersal.

Examines leaves and understands that they need light to produce food for the plant to grow.

Through knowledge, observation and investigation, puts together the stages in the life cycle of a flowering plant.

Applies what has been learned to understand the importance of green plants in an ecosystem, and their value to humans as a source of food.

Investigates the main factors affecting plant growth – light, water, temperature.

Understands the functions of the root.

Carries out germination tests.

Year 6

Variation and classification

Nursery/Reception

Identifies self as a child.

Notices similarities with other children – body parts and body functions.

Looking for variation among flowers.

Recognises differences, such as features, size, preferences.

Becomes aware of similarities and differences between familiar living things.

Groups animals by observing number of legs, how they move and body covering.

Groups plants by observing colour of flower, size of seed and texture of leaf.

Is able to devise keys for others to use for identification purposes.

Begins to understand the importance of grouping and classifying plants and animals.

Becomes increasingly aware of the diversity among plants and animals.

Begins to use more challenging criteria for grouping plants and animals, such as type of seed dispersal and feeding methods of animals.

Can interpret simple keys for identification purposes.

Year 6

Living things in their environment

Nursery/Reception

→ Notices that there is a variety of plants and animals in familiar environments.

→ Discovers that different environments, such as a pond, a hedgerow or a field, have different plants and animals living in them.

Becomes aware that living things require a specific place in which to live.

Investigates ways in which plants and animals are suited to living in their particular habitat.

Begins to recognise the relationships between the plants and animals in a particular habitat.

Understands how feeding methods, adaptations of physical structure and life cycles relate to specific habitats.

Identifying ways in which plants are suited to living in a particular habitat.

Is aware of the importance of green plants in a food chain and recognises the feeding relationships in an ecosystem.

Understands the valuable role some micro-organisms have in breaking down waste, and how we benefit from their activities.

Understands that there are also harmful micro-organisms and is aware of precautions that can be taken to avoid their effects.

Begins to appreciate the wide diversity of plant and animal life, the delicate balance that exists among living things and the responsibility of humans to preserve the environment.

Year 6

Progression in Materials and their Properties

Nursery/Reception

Explores everyday materials (safely).

Recognises and names familiar materials.

Can collect together items of the same material.

Grouping rocks according to their origins.

Begins to talk about similarities and differences between familiar materials.

Is aware of the different uses of familiar materials.

Investigates an increasing range of simple properties of materials.

Groups materials according to their properties.

Understands that some materials are found naturally.

Begins to link the properties of materials with their uses.

Investigates a wider range of materials and their properties.

Makes comparisons of materials according to their properties.

Can identify common solids, liquids and gases.

Examines the differences between rock types and soil types.

Understands how the properties and behaviour of materials affect our everyday lives.

Begins to recognise the differences between solids, liquids and gases.

Can describe how the uses of materials relate directly to the properties of those materials.

Begins to consider the need to manage the Earth's resources and the opportunities for reusing and recycling.

Year 6

31

Changing materials

Nursery/Reception

Explores the changes that can be made to materials by handling them.

Observes changes occurring to materials in everyday situations, such as cooking.

Dissolving materials

A collection of everyday materials that are soluble in water.

Describes the changes made by heating or cooling everyday materials.

Investigates how mixing materials can bring about changes.

Begins to understand that temperature is a measure of how hot or cold things are.

Investigates the heating and cooling of materials and records the changes that take place.

Distinguishes between reversible changes and non-reversible changes.

Observes what happens to materials when they are burned and understands that the changes that take place are not reversible.

Investigates what happens to materials during the processes of dissolving, melting, boiling, condensing, freezing and evaporating. Understands that the changes that occur to materials during these processes can be reversed.

Can identify where evaporation and condensation occur in the water cycle.

Begins to understand that changes occur naturally in the environment and how these changes affect our lives.

Recognises how we use the processes of change for our own purposes, sometimes to the detriment of the environment (pollution of water).

Year 6

Separating mixtures of materials (Key Stage 2 only)

Year 3

Is aware that some materials exist as mixtures.

Examines mixtures consisting of different-sized solid particles.

Experiences separating mixtures of different-sized solid particles by sieving.

Mixes a variety of solids with water to investigate dissolving.

Understands that a solution consists of a liquid and a solid that has dissolved in that liquid.

Experiences filtering to separate insoluble solids from water.

Filtering a mixture of water and soil.

Recognises whether a material is soluble or insoluble in a liquid.

Recovers soluble materials from solutions by evaporation.

Investigates how much of a solid will dissolve in an amount of water; compares different soluble solids.

Applies knowledge and experience to identify instances where the separation of materials occurs in everyday life.

Year 6

A selection of equipment suitable for filtering.

Progression in Physical Processes

Is aware that electricity is used to power many things that we use every day.

Understands that electricity is dangerous and that safety measures are important.

Is aware of the functions of batteries, wires, bulbs and buzzers.

Nursery/Reception

Experiments with batteries, wires, bulbs and buzzers to construct simple circuits.

Discovers that a break in a circuit prevents any electrical device from working.

Understands that a complete circuit is necessary to make an electrical device work.

Learns how to control electrical devices using a switch.

Understands that symbols can be used to represent the elements of an electrical circuit.

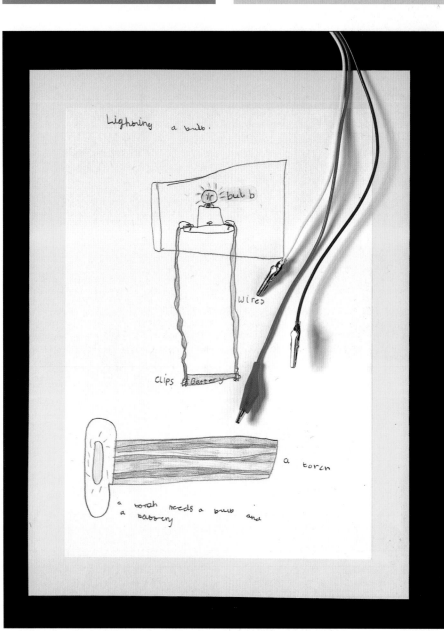

A diagram of a simple circuit.

Can represent a series circuit as a diagram, using symbols.

Can construct a series circuit from a diagram.

Investigates ways of varying current to make bulbs brighter or dimmer.

Becomes proficient in using equipment correctly and safely.

Develops an increasing understanding of electricity and the uses we make of it.

Year 6

forces and motion

Nursery/Reception → Is aware of different movements. →

Can describe different types of movement made by familiar things.

Observes changes in movements and can suggest causes.

Understands that pushes and pulls are examples of forces.

↓

Relates the movement of objects to the forces applied.

Recognises that forces can change the shape of objects.

↓

Explores the forces of attraction and repulsion of magnets.

Investigates gravitational forces.

Recognises friction and its effect on the movement of objects.

↓

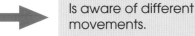

Push

I can push a wheelbarrow.

I can push a ball with my foot.

I can push a ball with a snooker cue.

pull

I can pull a sledge.

I can pull a cracker. Bang!!

I can pull out my wobbly tooth.

Duncan Oliphant

Identifying pushes and pulls.

Is aware of the forces involved during stretching and compressing.

Understands that forces act in particular directions.

Begins to recognise that when forces are balanced the object does not move.

Recognises the effects unbalanced forces can have on direction and speed of movement.

Develops an increasing awareness of forces and motion, relating knowledge and understanding to experiences of everyday life.

Year 6 ←

Light and sound

Nursery/Reception → Is aware of light and darkness.

→ Recognises different sounds.

Understands that sounds are heard when they enter the ear.

Explores different sources of sound.

Comparing light and sound.

Understands that light comes from various sources, including the Sun.

Understands that darkness is the absence of light.

Explores the effect of sound travelling through different materials.

Begins to apply ideas about sound to suggest how changes can be made by altering pitch or loudness.

Can describe the abstract idea that objects are seen when light from them enters our eyes.

Develops an increasing understanding of the physical phenomena of sound and light, relating experience and knowledge to everyday situations.

← Can describe changes in light and sound.

Can explain why sounds become fainter.

Understands that light travels from a source.

Uses this knowledge to investigate and explain the formation of shadows.

Explores the reflection of light.

Understands that sounds are made when objects vibrate.

Year 6

The Earth and beyond (Key Stage 2 only)

Year 3

Begins to understand the relationship between the Sun, Earth and Moon.

Knows that the Sun, Earth and Moon are approximately spherical.

Observes how the position of the Sun appears to change during the day.

Relates the changing positions of shadows to the apparent movement of the Sun.

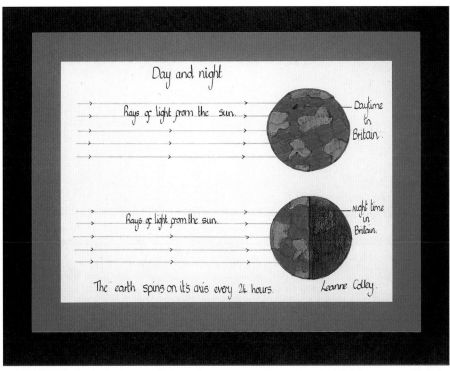

An explanation of day and night.

Understands that we experience day and night because the Earth spins around its axis.

Knows that our year is the time it takes the Earth to orbit the Sun.

Is aware that the Moon orbits the Earth approximately every 28 days.

Develops an increasing knowledge and understanding of the Earth and beyond.

Exploring the Earth orbiting the Sun.

Year 6

Progression in skills and processes

In Science:

- ☞ observation and communication are common to any science activity
- ☞ a combination of skills is practised and developed in any activity
- ☞ skills cannot be used in isolation from each other
- ☞ some skills, such as measuring, exploring and researching, are also developed in other areas of the Curriculum.

Exploring and observing

Nursery/Reception

Notices and shows interest in things all around – a pet, snow falling, an ice cube.

Notices, explores and talks about things and events – colours of autumn leaves, shininess of a metal, movement of a toy car.

Exploring involves finding out by examining and testing: discovering movement of muscles, the effect of magnets or the characteristics of mirrors.

Makes observations and comparisons; can observe similarities and differences: groups animals according to number of legs; identifies materials that are transparent; sounds that are soft. Can describe: the conditions for growing seedlings; the stretching of elastic; the lighting of a bulb in a circuit.

Observing involves using all appropriate senses to gather information about an object or process. All activities begin with observations and observing takes place throughout an activity. Children observe instinctively, but need help to develop their skills in a more focused and wide-ranging way by looking for similarities and differences, grouping and ordering, and relating their scientific knowledge to their observations. Children should have the opportunity to observe objects, such as a leaf, a rock or a piece of fabric; a sequence or process, such as a caterpillar feeding, chocolate melting or a spring stretching; and continuous happenings over a longer period, such as seasonal changes or an animal or plant growing. The use of hand lenses and other aids to observation should be encouraged.

Makes relevant observations when using equipment: measuring the rate of plant growth; how long it takes an ice cube to melt; the distance travelled by a toy car.

Provides explanations for observations: why a frog has webbed feet; the changes to clay during baking; why sounds become fainter.

Year 6

Develops a higher degree of observational skill when performing a task. Makes observations to identify parts of a flower; the differences between solids, liquids and gases; and the position of the Sun in relation to shadows. Repeats observations for checking purposes. Observes plants and animals in a habitat and relates observations to environmental factors; recognises evaporation and condensation in a variety of contexts; observes changes of current in an electrical circuit.

Predicting

Predicting is not guessing, but stating what might happen in the future, based on knowledge or evidence that is available; saying which boat will hold the greater cargo before sinking or which materials will melt when heated by hot water.

Hypothesising

Hypothesising is providing an explanation of what is happening, basing ideas on scientific knowledge or evidence available; the plant in the cupboard is not thriving because plants need light to make food.

Year 3

Begins to make simple predictions rather than guesses.

Uses previous knowledge and experience to make appropriate predictions when discussing and testing.

Understands that making a prediction is useful when planning an investigation.

Is aware that evidence from previous scientific experience is valuable when making a prediction.

Accepts that any discovery made during an investigation might not confirm a prediction.

Uses patterns in data to make predictions.

Confidently makes appropriate predictions based on scientific knowledge and understanding.

Year 6

Year 3

Offers simple explanations relating to observations.

Is aware that previous knowledge and experience are useful when explaining what is happening.

Accepts that any hypothesis may subsequently be proved wrong.

Understands that there could be several possible explanations suggested for any scientific happening.

Confidently provides explanations that may or may not be accurate, based on scientific knowledge and understanding.

Year 6

Communicating and recording

Communicating is the purposeful sharing of information by discussing, drawing or using various forms of writing. Observations can be drawn, notes and data of testing displayed and activities discussed and described.

Children need to be aware of the significance of communicating and recording. These are an important part of scientific procedure and a vital part of the learning process. Communicating helps to clarify ideas and inform others.

A science notebook can be used to collect notes, drawings of observations and measurements made during an activity or investigation.

Recording methods

Observational drawings
Drawings of an activity or investigation
Arrangement of objects for display
Scientific diagrams
Tables, charts and graphs
Descriptive writing
Notes and lists
Daily records
Cartoons
Headings
Labels
Explanations
Poems
Plans
Questions
Instructions for others
Artwork
Newsletters
Diaries
Posters
Leaflets
Class book
Notice boards

Nursery/Reception

Mostly oral communication, drawings and simple charts.

Talking, making lists, using sentences, drawings and tables.

Discussion and increased range of written evidence.

Extended discussion and detailed written evidence using tables, bar charts and graphs.

Detailed oral descriptions and reasoned argument. Systematic recording of observations and measurements. Data presented as line graphs where appropriate.

Year 6

THE HEART

RIGHT ATRIUM
receives deoxygenated
blood from the body

LEFT ATRIUM
receives oxygenated
blood from lungs

RIGHT VENTRICLE
pumps deoxygenated
blood to the lungs

LEFT VENTRICLE
pumps oxygenated
blood around the body

Your heart is a muscular pump. It is divided into right and left. Your heart is about the size of a clenched fist. The left side receives oxygenated blood from your lungs and then pumps it around your body. The right side pumps the blood back to the lungs to receive oxygen. Your blood travels in a one way system and carries materials to all the cells. Arteries carry blood away from the heart, veins carry blood to your heart.

Rachel Hedley.

A recording in the form of a labelled diagram and a written explanation.

40

Drawing conclusions, and applying knowledge and experience

Nursery/Reception

Talks about experiences of living things, objects and simple processes.

Drawing conclusions involves collecting together pieces of information, including any results, and making an appropriate decision. If seedlings in a cupboard and those in a refrigerator do not make good growth compared with those on a sunny window sill, one conclusion is that light and warmth are required for healthy growth.

Makes comparisons; describes what has happened and attempts a recount of what has been found out.

Applying knowledge and experience is the ability to use what has been learned to provide explanations; knowing that some flowers need insects to assist in pollination and relating this to the habits of the honey bee.

Uses observations and results, together with previous knowledge and experience, to describe what has been found out.

Uses observations and results to draw relevant conclusions; beginning to relate these to scientific knowledge, understanding and experience.

Draws conclusions that are consistent with evidence; relates conclusions to scientific knowledge and experience.

Communicating results in order to draw relevant conclusions.

Year 6

Assessment

Teachers are involved in a continuous, informal assessment of children's scientific developments and achievements during all science activities, through observing, listening to children, discussing their work, asking questions and evaluating written work. It is important, however, that assessment takes on a more structured role and that records and evidence are kept that give relevant information about each child's progress.

Assessment procedures should be incorporated into the planning of Science within the school and will be specific to the school. Procedures will be detailed in the school's Science policy and reference should be made to the whole-school assessment policy.

Teacher assessing child's knowledge and understanding of magnetism.

Purposes of assessment

- ☛ To indicate progress, showing how a child's knowledge and understanding of science is developing.
- ☛ To demonstrate progress in Experimental and Investigative Science.
- ☛ To record achievements, so that progress is acknowledged and motivation increased.
- ☛ To diagnose difficulties, so that planning can be revised and strategies for overcoming problems devised.
- ☛ To set new targets that enable children to move forward by means of a series of appropriate and challenging steps.
- ☛ To be able to communicate with parents, governors and local authorities, and inform them of a child's scientific development.

Questions to consider

- ☛ How will children's progress and development in this module of work be assessed?
- ☛ Which particular activities will provide opportunities for assessment?
- ☛ During an activity, will an individual or a group of children be assessed?
- ☛ Do the rest of the class understand that they must work independently of the teacher who is involved in the assessment procedure?
- ☛ Can children, who are not being assessed at the time, carry out their science task independently? Do they understand what to do? Can they obtain the equipment and materials they need?

Knowledge and understanding

The National Curriculum for Science provides guidelines for assessing a child's knowledge and understanding, and the development of skills, but scientific development is also determined by attitudes. Assessment of children's knowledge and understanding is best undertaken by:

☞ listening to them as they discuss their work
☞ asking carefully worded questions
☞ evaluating written work
☞ arranging test situations.

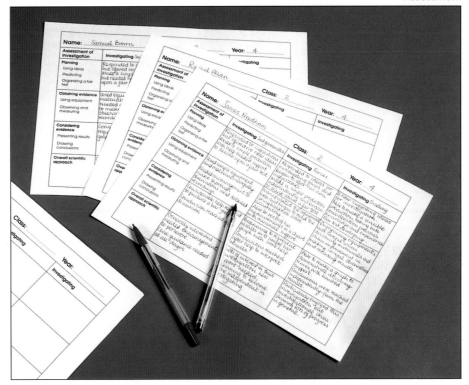

Teacher records of assessment.

Assessing skills and attitudes

☞ Provide a series of graded experimental and investigative tasks over the Key Stage with detailed criteria for assessment.

☞ Assess progress in Science by examining children's attitudes to their work. Does the child:
 – show curiosity and a desire to find out?
 – put forward ideas for experimenting?
 – make suggestions that can be investigated?
 – offer opinions?
 – find ways of organising a task independently, by searching out materials and equipment and making things where appropriate?
 – make decisions after considering evidence?
 – willingly revise ideas in the light of evidence collected?
 – collaborate successfully with others and allow for their points of view?
 – understand the importance of recording data carefully during an investigation, and do this without prompting?
 – persevere with a task until a successful outcome is reached?

Standard Assessment Tests

Teachers within a school, and possibly within a family of schools, need to discuss and moderate children's work so that consistency can be achieved. What a child is expected to achieve at each level needs to be determined and examples of children's work that show this can be identified.

Key Stage 2 Tasks and Tests

SATs (Standard Assessment Tests) are administered at the end of Key Stage 2.

Tasks are for children working at Levels 1 and 2 and can be administered in groups. Tests are externally marked and results returned to schools for communicating to parents. Under the current arrangements, children are supplied with test booklets and are asked to provide written answers that assess their knowledge and their understanding.

Teacher assessment, together with a child's SATs results, indicates their overall achievement at the end of the Key Stage.

Recording and reporting

Record keeping

Record keeping will vary from school to school but it is important to develop a whole-school approach in order to achieve continuity between the subject areas.

Consider some of the following questions when establishing systems and procedures for the recording and reporting of Science.

☛ Why record?
☛ Who is the record for?
☛ What will be recorded?
☛ When will the recording take place?
☛ How often?
☛ Where will the records be kept?

☛ How will they be organised?
☛ How much evidence will be kept?
☛ Who has access to the records?
☛ How will you ensure continuity and consistency in recording?
☛ What happens to the records at the end of the Year or Key Stage?

It is important to have evidence of all the Science that has taken place:
– throughout the whole school
– in individual classes
– with each child
in order to:
– ensure the broad and balanced delivery of the Science Curriculum
– ensure continuity and consistency in coverage for each year group/class
– build up an individual profile of achievement and progress.

Records need to be simple, meaningful and not too time-consuming. As well as recording areas of the Science Curriculum that have been taught and assessed, they should also indicate children's experiences, achievements and attitudes and be a combination of teacher records and children's work.

It is important to have records of:
– areas of the National Curriculum that have been covered and other science-related information that has been presented to the children
– the level of knowledge and understanding attained by individual children in Science
– experiences presented to the children to enhance their understanding of science, as well as experiences in other Curriculum areas with a strong science link
– skills specific to Science that have been practised, developed and assessed; level of competence when carrying out investigations; scientific attitudes including level of interest shown, and development of scientific thinking.

Methods of recording and reporting

In addition to formal recording and reporting to parents, governors, OFSTED and the wider community through parents evenings, end-of-year reports, etc, there are various ways in which the range of science achievements within a school can be demonstrated.

☛ Photographs and video recordings showing activities and investigations, including long-term projects, children's work, special events which have a scientific theme, visits to science and field centres and visits to school by experts in an area of science.

☛ A collection of work to represent science in school over a period of time. This can reach a wider audience through open days, displays, an exhibition, drama, or demonstrations.

☛ A class collection to show a term's activities could be presented as a book, special display or class assembly.

☛ An individual portfolio put together by each child over a period of time that can be shown to other children, parents and visitors.

Using the evidence

Perhaps the most important use of the evidence gathered is to plan the children's next stage of development. It should help to identify children's strengths and weaknesses in their science knowledge, skills and attitudes, and assist the teacher in preparing differentiated work appropriate to the needs and abilities of the children.

Evidence gathered and recorded over time can be used to write a summary of the child's progress and presented in the form of an annual report to parents; or can be shared with parents and children at open-evenings to provide essential feedback and to help set targets for future work.

Display

A display is most effective if children can be involved in planning, designing and creating it, and are encouraged to discuss the information it contains and make comments. A science display should evolve as discoveries are made and information is added. Data collected could be regularly updated to give a workshop feel while testing continues. If possible, use a contribution from every child.

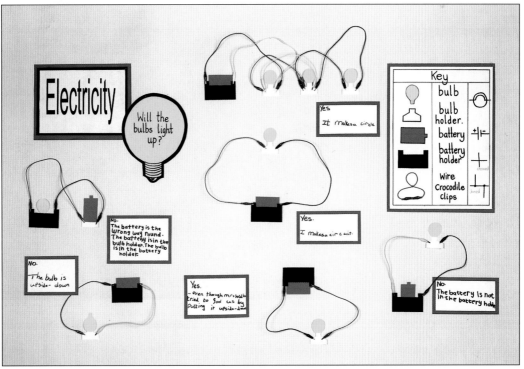

A display consolidating work on electrical circuits.

Where to display science work
☞ In classrooms, corridors, the school hall and the library.
☞ Locally, at the community centre, in shop windows, at the local garden centre.

Why display science?
☞ To raise the profile of, and create interest in, science.
☞ To give importance to children's work.
☞ To communicate information.
☞ To encourage high standards of science work.
☞ To consolidate and celebrate learning achieved.

What to display
☞ Collections of seeds, plants in pots, rocks, materials, tools, musical instruments, pictures, books.
☞ Information on the work of notable scientists, different habitats, space research, the water cycle.
☞ Children's work relating to a theme or project that could be arranged around a model, an incubator, or a demonstration.
☞ Children's work describing the process of an investigation, communicating the results to other classes.

☞ Materials, equipment and tools for hands-on experimenting; mirrors, magnets and electrical circuitry. Provide labels, questions and appropriate books.
☞ Information relating to children's successes and environmental projects, participation in competitions, energy-saving schemes, recycling initiatives, maintaining and creating habitats in the school grounds.
☞ News items reporting on local and global issues, new discoveries, latest scientific research, and seasonal events.

Special needs

Every child, regardless of gender, race or ability, should be encouraged to enjoy and take part in science activities and be given the opportunity to experience, investigate, understand and work together with others. Teachers should refer to the school's policy for special needs and liaise with the special needs coordinator when appropriate.

Learning difficulties

Children need science tasks appropriate to their ability.

- ☞ The language or mathematical demand of an activity can be reduced as appropriate.
- ☞ Practical tasks can be simplified.
- ☞ Extra support can be given, in small stages, during investigations.

IT providing a useful recording method.

Behavioural problems

Science activities can provide interest and win a child's attention where other subjects might fail. However, there is greater opportunity for disruption when children are collaborating or engaged in practical tasks, possibly outdoors. Extra safety precautions and adult support might be necessary. Where attention span is limited, targets will need to be discussed and set.

Physical difficulties

In practical situations, provision needs to be made so that all children can take part in classroom investigations and outdoor work. Access to equipment, materials and other children should be considered. Children might be helped by:

- ☞ extra observational aids
- ☞ movement or rearrangement of furniture
- ☞ lightweight or adapted equipment

- ☞ practical work that is relatively less onerous
- ☞ communication aids
- ☞ use of IT for recording purposes
- ☞ tactile emphasis.

Children with hearing or visual impairments will need special arrangements to access as much as possible of the Light and sound sections of the Science Programmes of Study.

Very able children

Children demonstrating above average ability in Science will need specially extended tasks that challenge their thinking and develop their understanding. They can be encouraged to plan investigations, work independently, discuss, research and collaborate with other children and with adults. Interested children can follow current science developments by reading newspapers and journals and using CD-ROMS and the Internet to research and access information.

Differentiation

Differentiation involves adjusting your teaching to meet the learning needs of individual children. It is not possible to match every task to the ability of every child, but there are certain strategies that can be adopted to help ensure that most children are working at the right level.

Planning

Science planning should allow for a variety of teaching methods. All children should experience, as appropriate, class teaching, working with a partner, collaborating within a group and working independently. Class teaching includes:

- discussion and brainstorming
- demonstrations
- instruction
- preparation for an activity
- reporting back and evaluating an activity.

Groups will vary in size and nature. They can be organised according to ability, friendship groupings or other criteria. Each group member should play an important and equal part in an activity.

Groups can be organised so:

- all are working on the same activity and will discuss the results within the group
- all are carrying out the same activity and will contribute information and perhaps data in a class discussion and evaluation at the end
- they are working on a different activity within a common theme and will make a contribution to the whole project
- where resources are limited, each group can work in turn on a different task – all children experiencing the same activity over a period of time.

Continuity and progression

Continuity
The National Curriculum for Science provides a framework that facilitates continuity of content across and within the Key Stages. A well-planned Science programme provides a clear and logical sequence of work within a school so that gaps and unnecessary repetition are avoided.

Continuity of content, and methods of assessment and recording will be an integral part of planning.

Liaison between colleagues is important, both within a school and between schools.

Progression
Progression in science learning is achieved by matching work to the children, and providing a sequence of increasingly challenging activities. Smooth progression in understanding and the development of ideas, skills and good scientific procedure is important.

Strategies that assist differentiation

- Study assessments, records and other available information to identify a child's achievements and difficulties.
- Where all children are to be involved in the same task, group according to ability, setting targets at different levels.
- Provide a series of graded tasks on a similar theme, bringing groups together for a whole-class discussion of results and discoveries.
- Where an investigation is open-ended, allow children to work at their individual level.
- In mixed-ability groups, encourage children to support each other when planning and carrying out an investigation, each recording individually.
- Encourage independent working during activities so that teacher support can be concentrated within a particular group of children.
- Allow for different methods of recording.
- Have available support material for children to use.
- Adapt the mathematical demands of an investigation.
- Incorporate appropriate extension activities into the planning.

Cross-curricular links

The teaching and learning of Science benefits from the numerous cross-curricular links that can be made. In so doing, it is able to both utilise and present 'real' opportunities for practising skills specific to other Curriculum areas.

Mathematics

Using and applying
Investigative work in Science provides opportunities for using and applying mathematics in real and relevant situations. Children will use mathematical equipment, check and consider results, identify patterns, develop strategies and reasoning and use mathematical language and written forms of communication.

Number
Number is used for counting, calculating, estimating, fractions, percentages, and comparing proportions. Calculators are often appropriate.

Shape, space and measurement
Occasionally it is appropriate to describe shapes and patterns and to recognise symmetry. Frequently mathematical units of measurement are used; accurate reading of instruments and scales is necessary.

Handling data
During scientific investigations children are collecting, representing and interpreting data using graphs and diagrams, and understanding and using probability.

English

Speaking and listening
Science provides opportunities for practising and developing linguistic skills through listening, discussing, expressing and sharing ideas, explaining, responding to other points of view, reporting and describing observations, and increasing spoken vocabulary. Scientific knowledge and ideas can be presented to different audiences through drama and role-play.

Reading
Extending scientific vocabulary through appropriate scientific texts; finding information, using reference material, newspapers and indexes; stories and poetry with science themes.

Writing
Science provides opportunities for written communication, responding to scientific observations, ideas and investigations: reports, instructions, explanations, diaries, notes; using script for notes and print for labelling.

Investigating the properties of building materials, links Geography and Science.

Geography

There are strong links through environmental issues:
- study of different localities, looking at diversity of life, materials for building, water pollution, rocks and soils
- rivers, seas and the water cycle
- weather, especially temperatures
- environmental change.

History

Opportunities are provided for looking at history from a scientific perspective – as in materials used for clothes, buildings, roads, artefacts and food. Also:
- scientists and scientific eras
- health and medicine
- industry and transport
- developing technology
- changing environments.

Physical Education

Science provides strong links with health, exercise and the workings of the human body. Scientific ideas and activities can provide stimuli for expression through dance.

Measuring pulse rate.

Religious Education

Opportunities arise in Science for discovering the significance of plants, animals, materials, light and sound in different religions.

Design and Technology

Sometimes it is appropriate for science to be carried out through Design and Technology:

- making products to test a scientific idea
- selecting materials and relating their properties to their uses when designing and making
- relating knowledge and understanding of electricity and forces to designing and making
- working with food and textiles.

Art

Science provides opportunities for recording from direct experience and developing observational drawing, as well as experimenting with light and materials such as paper, clay, textiles and charcoal.

A textile recording of a flying ant.

Using specially designed vehicles to investigate forces.

Information and Communication Technology

Aspects of science can be explored through information technology; equipment and software can be used to communicate, organise, reorganise and analyse scientific ideas and information.

Exploring musical sounds.

Music

Science provides opportunities for exploring how musical sounds are created. Experimenting with a range of instruments and exploring pitch and loudness can provide inspiration for composing and performing, and can identify themes for listening and appraising.

49

Environmental education

The ultimate aim of environmental education is to sustain our planet and its resources for future generations.

Environmental education provides opportunities for:
- scientific experiences out of doors
- developing scientific skills
- encouraging observation and sensory awareness
- arousing interest and increasing motivation
- working collaboratively
- tackling real problems
- making decisions
- developing respect and a sense of ownership of learning.

The natural world

Through science, children discover the natural world and find out how we make use of the Earth's resources.

Scientific activity and investigation can take place in the school grounds, the immediate neighbourhood, at field and residential centres, and on day visits.

Learning **ABOUT** the environment increases knowledge of plants, animals, materials and processes.

Learning **IN** the environment uses the environment as a resource for first-hand experiences and development of skills.

Learning **FOR** the environment encourages development of values and attitudes, and helps children to make decisions concerning the future of the planet.

Areas of school life that relate to the environment

Real issues
- Local and national:
  - oil spills
  - road building
- Agenda 21*

Extra-curricular
- Science clubs – recycling, gardening, wildlife projects
- National societies, such as YOC (Young Ornithologists Club) and Watch

National Curriculum
- Science makes an important contribution to environmental education

Special events
- School grounds day
- Science activity day
- Competitions

Whole-school ethos
- Environmental policy
- Children's charter

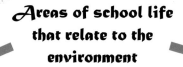

Community projects
- Recycling initiative
- Wildlife monitoring
- Habitat creation
- Tree planting

* Agenda 21 came out of the Rio Earth Summit of 1992. 179 nations agreed to a blueprint for saving and caring for the Earth.

Experimental and Investigative Science

Explorations and investigations related to environmental issues:

☞ investigating the germination conditions required of different seeds and relating these to the survival rate of the plants

☞ exploring the diversity and relationships of plants and animals within an ecosystem

☞ investigating the rate of decay of a range of waste materials.

Scientific investigation during a day visit to Llechwedd slate quarries, North Wales.

Life Processes and Living Things

Life processes

☞ Observing and finding similarities and differences of feeding methods, growth patterns, methods of movement and means of reproduction of plants and of animals.

☞ Developing an understanding of, and respect for, living things and the variety of life.

Green plants as organisms

☞ The functions and needs of plants.

☞ Factors affecting the survival of plants.

☞ Degrees of success among plants.

☞ Human influence on the survival or destruction of a species.

Variation and classification

☞ Diversity among plants and animals.

☞ The importance of each individual species.

☞ Endangered species.

Living things in their environment

☞ The importance of preserving and creating habitats for the continuation of particular plants and animals.

☞ Food chains and the consequences to a species of any disruption or contamination of a food chain.

☞ The role of plants in feeding the world.

☞ The importance of micro-organisms in breaking down waste.

Materials and their Properties

Grouping and classifying materials

☞ Uses made of the Earth's resources.

☞ Supplies of sustainable and non-sustainable materials.

☞ How different rocks are obtained and used.

☞ Soil fertility.

☞ Management of resources and the production of waste.

☞ Behaviour of greenhouse gases and the ozone layer.

Changing materials

☞ Temperatures and global warming.

☞ The water cycle and water pollution and conservation.

☞ The effects of burning on the atmosphere.

Separating mixtures of materials

☞ Removing pollutants.

☞ Filtration processes in the treatment of water.

Physical Processes

Electricity

☞ Ways of producing electricity.

☞ Use of fossil fuels compared with sustainable methods of energy production.

Forces

☞ Linking the effects of forces and living things.

Light

☞ Its importance to plants and therefore to animals.

The Earth and beyond

☞ The Earth's place in the universe.

☞ Our dependence on the Sun and the influence of the Moon.

☞ The importance of maintaining the air, land and water resources of our planet to sustain diversity of life.

Health education

The National Curriculum for Science provides the knowledge whereby children can begin to understand the role they play in keeping healthy. With relevant information, children can develop positive attitudes and make decisions relating to their personal lifestyles.

Key Stage 1

Pupils should be given opportunities to consider ways in which science is relevant to their personal health.

Programme of Study	Aspects of health education	Areas of experience
Life processes ☞ Humans move, feed, grow, use their senses and reproduce.	**Healthy living**	Functions of the body – moving, feeding, growing, using senses, reproducing.
Humans as organisms ☞ Name the external parts of the body.	**The body**	Parts of the body; keeping clean.
☞ Humans have senses that enable them to be aware of the world around them.	**Using the senses**	Valuing and caring for the body.
☞ Humans need food and water to stay alive.	**Food and feeding**	The need for food and water; different foods, healthy eating.
☞ Taking exercise and eating the right types and amount of food help humans to keep healthy.	**Taking exercise**	The importance of exercise.
☞ The role of drugs as medicines.	**Drugs as medicines**	The safe use of medicines.
☞ Humans produce babies and these babies grow into children and then into adults.	**Family life**	Stages in the human life cycle; family members; caring for each other.
Variation and classification ☞ Recognising similarities and differences between themselves and other pupils.	**Other people**	Similarities and differences among people; sensitivity towards others.

Key Stage 2

Pupils should be given opportunities to relate their understanding of science to their personal health.

Programme of Study	Aspects of health education	Areas of experience
Life processes ☞ There are life processes, including nutrition, movement, growth and reproduction, common to animals including humans.	**A healthy lifestyle**	Growing up; functions of the body.
Humans as organisms ☞ The functions of teeth and the importance of dental care.	**Hygiene**	Care of teeth, hair and skin.
☞ Food is needed for activity and growth; an adequate and varied diet is needed to keep healthy. ☞ Nearly all food chains start with a green plant.	**Food and nutrition**	Different types and purposes of food; eating patterns, digesting food; growth patterns; micro-organisms in food and digestion; developing good habits in food preparation and eating.
☞ Micro-organisms exist – many may be beneficial, while others may be harmful.	**Medicine**	Illnesses caused by micro-organisms. The use of vaccinations in preventing disease.
☞ The structure of the heart and how it acts as a pump. ☞ Blood circulates in the body through arteries and veins. ☞ The effect of exercise and rest on pulse rate. ☞ Skeletons and muscles support bodies and help them to move.	**Exercise**	Importance of regular exercise in relation to the whole body.
☞ The main stages of the human life cycle.	**Family life** **Sex education**	Caring and cooperation within families. Developing an awareness of body functions and changes.
☞ Tobacco, alcohol and other drugs can have harmful effects.	**Misuse of drugs**	The effects of substances on the body; development of positive attitudes.

Together these contribute to social, moral and emotional development; building up self-esteem and preparing for puberty.

Industrial and economic awareness

Science has close links with industry. In our everyday life, the scientific processes we perform and many of the things we use, can be traced to an industrial operation.

Relating to industry through science can provide a relevant and interesting focus that can stimulate and motivate, develop skills and extend knowledge. Children's perceptions of industry are usually second-hand – gleaned from newspaper reports, television programmes and conversations with adults. To increase their awareness and encourage positive attitudes, links can be forged with local companies, visits can be organised and experts can be invited into school to talk and perhaps demonstrate their skills. Teacher placements can be arranged from which beneficial liaisons between industry and education may develop.

Through links with industry, children will develop an understanding of the importance of science in the manufacture and distribution of the things they need; the use of finite resources and the disposal of unwanted materials; energy requirements and the need to conserve; as well as the cost and value of everyday requirements.

Mini-enterprises

Encourage children to launch their own mini-enterprise. It will give them first-hand experience of working cooperatively, investigating, testing, making decisions, costing, creating and marketing a product or a service. Projects include:

Recycling school waste.

- collecting and packeting seeds
- producing bird feeders or boxes
- packing and distributing bird or pet food
- testing materials and making bags, glove puppets, simple toys
- recycling and the management of waste.

The school environment

Identify the scientific processes in which adults connected with your school are involved day-to-day. People such as:
- secretary
- caretaker
- cleaner
- cook
- groundspeople
- people involved in deliveries – post, milk, other supplies
- maintenance people – electrical equipment, computers, telephones
- building workers.

Economic aspects to consider include the following.
- What types of materials and equipment are used?
- Who decides what to buy?
- How are decisions made?
- Do products give value for money?
- Are environmental factors taken into consideration?
- What is the situation regarding disposal of unwanted items and materials?

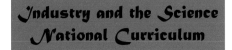
Industry and the Science National Curriculum

Experimental and Investigative Science
Industrial processes involve researching and testing materials and products, and applying processes. Children can identify examples of fair testing, precise working and accurate measuring. They can understand the need for careful collection and presentation of data, and appreciate the value of information technology.

Life Processes and Living Things

Food	Growing, processing, selling	Farms, factories, shops
Leisure	Fitness, exercise	Leisure centres
Health	Medicines, treatment	Medical centres, pharmaceuticals
Plants	Agriculture, horticulture, fruit growing	Farms, garden centres, food producers, research establishments
Micro-organisms	Baking, brewing, health, waste disposal, soil fertility	Bakeries, breweries, water-treatment works, medical centres, farms, pharmaceuticals

Materials and their Properties

Materials: using, making, disposing	Textiles, metals, plastics, building materials, floor coverings, paper	Research establishments, manufacturing companies, building operations, packaging plants, waste-disposal sites
Rocks: extracting and using	Local stone	Quarries, opencast mines, stonemasons, producers of building materials
Soils	Types and characteristics	Farms, research establishments
Gases	Fuel, drinks, machines, transport, medical	Gas industry, manufacturing companies
Processes	Mixing, dissolving, heating, cooling, evaporating, melting, freezing, burning, condensing, filtering	Water-treatment works, manufacturing companies, food preservation, chemical industry, pharmaceuticals, petro-chemicals

Physical Processes

Electricity	Production and appliances	Power stations, manufacturing companies, micro-electronics
Forces and motion	Construction, transport, manufacturing, sports, defence	Building operations, factories, structures, transport systems
Light	Photography, lenses, lighting systems, fibre-optics, lasers	Photographers' studios, factories, opticians, television studios
Sound	Musical instruments, music production, pollution	Manufacturers, radio stations, audiometrics
The Earth and beyond	Telescopes, space travel	Space research establishments, observatories

Information technology and science

Scientists today use a wide range of technological aids to assist and enhance their work. Many time-consuming and laborious tasks can be carried out speedily and more efficiently. Images can be created, results and findings analysed, and data displayed. Access to information and direct communication with colleagues worldwide is now possible.

The increasing availability of technological aids in primary schools today can make important contributions to Science teaching.

The National Curriculum for Information and Communication Technology and for Science provides guidelines, and reference should be made to your school's policy for Information and Communication Technology.

The common requirements of the Science Programme of Study state that: 'Pupils should be given opportunities, where appropriate, to develop and apply their information technology capability in their study of science.'

The Programmes of Study for both Key Stages 1 and 2 state: 'Pupils should be given opportunities to use information technology to collect, store, retrieve and present scientific information.'

Computers

Children can be encouraged to practise, apply and develop their computer skills during science activities. They can look at different ways of scientific working and compare computer methods with other methods they have used.

Word processing
- Planning and organising ideas.
- Writing reports.
- Preparing work for display.
- Writing instructions.
- Creating labels for information and display using different fonts and styles.

Desktop publishing
- Preparing and presenting information and results, communicating to a variety of audiences.

Internet and electronic mail
- Retrieving information.
- Communication.

Handling information
- Collecting, storing, sorting and retrieving information; looking for patterns and trends.
- Creating and using a branching database, or yes/no key.
- Using a commercially prepared database of information for sorting, decision making and investigation.

Spreadsheets
- Displaying information for decision making, and for problem-solving.

Models and simulations
- Employing appropriate software to use and apply scientific knowledge.

Control technology
- Using computers to control scientific 3D working devices; operating switches and gears.

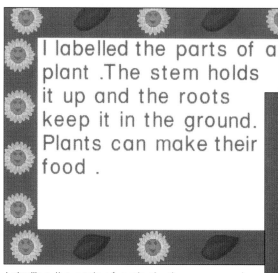

I labelled the parts of a plant .The stem holds it up and the roots keep it in the ground. Plants can make their food .

Labelling the parts of a plant using a computer.

Video films

These can be obtained to show images that cannot be experienced at first hand.

- ☛ **Slow motion** pictures of things that happen quickly – the flight of an insect, falling objects.
- ☛ **Speeded-up images** – the opening of a leaf bud, the germination of a seed, the evaporation of a puddle, the formation of crystals.
- ☛ **Animals and plants** in their natural habitats.
- ☛ **Processes** that cannot safely be performed in the classroom, perhaps because of high temperatures or dangerous materials.
- ☛ **Industrial aspects of science.**
- ☛ **The internal workings of the human body.**

Photocopiers

Can be used:

- ☛ to reproduce children's work for communicating ideas and data
- ☛ to produce images to enhance displays. Grasses and leaves can be photocopied and used to demonstrate variations in shape and structure.

Electronic instruments

Useful when accurate and speedy results are required – a balance for measuring the weight of growing chicks, a thermometer for detecting the temperature of soil, water or air.

Cameras and video cameras

Children can use these to record:

- ☛ sequences of plant growth:
  - the development of flowers, seeds or bulbs like poppy, honesty and hyacinth
  - a tree through the seasons
- ☛ stages in the life cycles of animals
- ☛ changes occurring within a local habitat
- ☛ before and after pictures showing changes to materials
- ☛ stages in processes, such as evaporation and freezing
- ☛ evidence collected during investigations and demonstrations.

Photography as a means of recording the development of a plant.

CD-ROM

An increasing amount and variety of scientific information is available on CD-ROM. Useful areas for children to research could include:

- ☛ plant and animal life
- ☛ the human body
- ☛ food chains and habitats
- ☛ classification of living things
- ☛ uses of materials
- ☛ physical processes
- ☛ famous scientists.

OHP

An OHP can be used:

- ☛ when a controllable source of light is required
- ☛ to create shadows
- ☛ for children to share ideas, results or conclusions with a wider audience.

Resources

It is important to develop an efficient system of storing and managing resources. A centrally stored bank of resources is ideal but regularly used items, such as lenses and room thermometers, should be available in classrooms. A reserve supply of consumable materials will need to be checked regularly.

All children should understand the system for locating, removing, using and returning anything they require in science activities. This could involve a labelling system or a specially prepared catalogue, perhaps with items arranged alphabetically and a code explaining where they are kept. Tracking items that are in use is important.

Children can play a valuable part in maintaining resources, with responsibility for checking supplies, keeping shelves clean and tidy, and sorting and collecting materials.

Questions to ask

- Are the science resources easily accessible to children?
- Are they stored safely?
- Can children find what they need independently?
- What is the procedure for borrowing and returning equipment and materials?
- How long can equipment, borrowed from the central store, be kept in classrooms?
- How can missing resources be tracked down?
- What is the procedure when supplies of consumables run low?
- What is the procedure for reporting broken or damaged equipment?
- How quickly are staff alerted to new materials entering school? (Information about exhibitions, competitions, local events, environmental matters, promotional literature, new books.)
- Are children able to spend time working outside on appropriate activities?
- In what ways can children be involved in organising and looking after the science resources?

Resources checklist

- Books, charts and pictures, promotional material produced by companies and agencies, videotapes and software all enhance the teaching of Science. Teachers need to know how these are related to the National Curriculum and where they can be found.
- Working areas where science activities can take place are important. Flat surfaces are needed where ongoing tests can be observed and displays arranged.
- Surfaces near windows, in darker places, and at different temperatures are necessary. Access to a freezer, to boiling water and to methods of heating is essential in order to deliver all areas of the Science National Curriculum.
- Safe outdoor areas within the school grounds enable a wide range of activities to take place away from the classroom. Wildlife and garden areas provide a variety of habitats that children can experience at first hand.

An efficiently organised central store cupboard.

Essential equipment

Hand lenses
Centimetre rulers
Tape measures
Graduated rulers
Metre sticks
Trundle wheels
Volumetric measures, graduated in litres and millilitres
Balances and weights
Forcemeters
Stopwatches
Thermometers of different types
Droppers
Syringes
Petri dishes
Funnels
Sieves
Heating ring
Large transparent plastic containers
Plastic buckets and bowls
Magnets
Mirrors
Prisms
Directional compasses

Bulbs and bulb holders
Battery holders
Crocodile clips
Wire and springs
Marbles
Torches
Plastic tubing
Blindfolds
Paper fasteners
Paper clips
Clipboards
Bulldog clips

Extra equipment
Binocular microscope
Electronic balance
Electronic temperature probe
Incubator
Watering cans
Cooking equipment
Gardening tools

Tools
Screwdrivers
Scissors
Wire cutters

Consumable materials
Sugar
Salt
Flour
Bath crystals
Peas, beans, lentils
Food colouring
Sand and gravel
Peat-free compost
Aluminium foil
Elastic bands
Cling film
String and glue
Kitchen paper
Candles
Cooking oil
Vinegar
Lemon juice
Bicarbonate of soda
Modelling clay
Washing-up liquid
Balloons

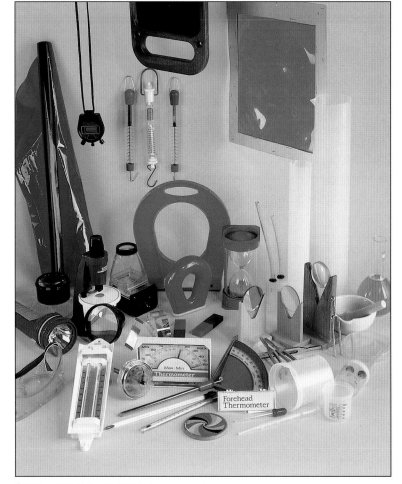

Some essential equipment.

Items to collect

Plastic pots
Small glass jars (identical)
Aluminium dishes
Plastic sweet jars
Newspapers
Plant pots
Plastic spoons
Plastic bottles
Corks
Polystyrene

Collections

Fabrics
Types of wood
Types of metal
Types of plastic
Building materials
Packaging materials
Seeds
Classroom plants
Rocks
Shells

Multicultural issues

Through science, children are discovering the similar needs and contrasting ways of life of people throughout the world. In caring for the environment, they are seeking to preserve the diversity of the planet for everyone.

Science resources should reflect different cultures, regardless of the composition of the class. Books, pictures and other materials need to be carefully selected.

There are opportunities to encourage an awareness of different cultures through the sensitive use of resources such as:
- fabrics and clothes
- toys
- food and plants
- tools
- cooking methods and equipment
- transport and travel

A demonstration of Indian cooking methods and equipment.

- machines
- areas of work
- festivals – use of materials, music and light.

Experts to invite into school

A variety of people are specially trained to come into schools and work with children, mainly in the fields of health and safety:
- dental nurse
- nutritionist
- health worker
- nurse – hygiene and sex education
- road, rail, water, fire, gas and electricity safety experts.

Schemes where scientists visit primary schools operate in some parts of the country.

Other people to invite could be professionals, enthusiasts and amateurs.
These may include:
- gardener
- naturalist
- explorer/traveller
- environmentalist
- ranger
- Wildlife Trust representative
- recycling officer
- pollution expert
- water filtration expert
- plumber
- engineer

- craftspeople – woodworker, metal worker, stonemason
- laboratory technician
- researcher
- sports person/athlete
- designer
- baker
- food producer
- musician
- astronomer.

It is important to include people who represent different cultures.

Safety

It is the responsibility of the class teacher to ensure a safe working environment. Children should be aware of any risks and dangers and understand the importance of working safely at all times. Frequent reminders need to be given to reinforce safe working procedures. However, the children can also be involved in establishing science safety rules themselves.

Reference should be made to the health and safety section of the school's Science policy as well as the school's safety policy. A useful and comprehensive guide to safety in Science is *Be Safe,* published by the Association for Science Education.

A safety poster.

Safety checklist

- Are children aware of the importance of working safely at all times?
- Are they familiar with first-aid procedures?
- Do they understand the importance of washing their hands after handling materials, equipment, plants and animals?
- Are they alerted to instances when plants and animals might cause allergic reactions?
- Do they know that many plants and substances they encounter are poisonous?
- Are children encouraged to handle all equipment carefully to avoid accidents?
- Are they prevented from lifting heavy loads?
- Have children been warned of the dangers of inhaling substances, such as solvents, and the importance of using aerosols in a well-ventilated room?
- Do the children know that nothing must be tasted unless special permission has been given?

- When food is being prepared and eaten, are high standards of hygiene maintained?
- Are children aware that when using tools, extra care must be taken and that eyes are particularly vulnerable?
- When glass items are used, do children realise the added dangers and understand the procedure to follow if any glass is broken?
- Where high temperatures are involved, are appropriate precautions taken?
- Are children aware of the procedure to be followed in the case of fire?
- Do they understand the safe procedures to adopt when using electrical appliances?
- Is there a code of behaviour for children to follow when they are working outside the classroom?

Pioneers of science

The processes we rely on and the things we use and take for granted every day of our lives, have developed from the ideas, the discoveries and the achievements of past scientists. Contributions to science, great and small, by people famous and unknown, provide inspiration and information that others can use, develop and extend. The process continues and children should be encouraged to feel they are a part of this progress.

Men and women today are working in every field of science. People of all nationalities meet and collaborate, exchanging ideas and advancing developments in areas, such as health, pollution prevention, manufacturing and space research.

Ancient Greeks 500–300 BC
The Ancient Greeks were great thinkers; they made important contributions to the development of scientific knowledge, particularly in the areas of astronomy and medicine. They made significant observations, raised questions and tried to understand the principles of science. Sometimes their conclusions were wrong, but often they were accurate. The Greeks understood that the Earth revolves around the Sun and that the Moon reflects sunlight.

Galileo Galilei 1564–1642
Italian astronomer
Galileo Galilei developed the newly invented telescope as an aid to studying stars and planets. His observations brought about a change of ideas in astronomy.

Sir Isaac Newton 1642–1727
English scientist and philosopher
Isaac Newton demonstrated important discoveries in physics. He described the force of gravity when he realised that the Earth attracts all objects of smaller mass; showed how sunlight can be split into the colours of the spectrum; and explored the movement of everyday things. He is considered by present-day scientists to be the founder of modern physics.

Carolus Linnaeus 1707–1778
Swedish botanist
Linnaeus realised it was necessary to classify plants and animals for identification and comparison, which he did according to their structure; the accepted system of classification used today is developed from his work.

Edward Jenner 1749–1823
English doctor
Jenner realised that milkmaids who were exposed to cowpox did not catch the more virulent smallpox. People given mild doses of cowpox were saved from the disease, a process later termed 'vaccination' by Pasteur (*vacca* is Latin for cow). Smallpox was eradicated throughout the world in 1977.

Michael Faraday 1791–1867
English chemist and physicist
Faraday made discoveries in several areas of physics and chemistry, notably in magnetism and electricity. He made electricity using a magnet and coil of wire – the principle behind electricity production in power stations today. A great experimental scientist, he kept detailed notes of all his experiments and thoughts, which have been of great importance to others. Faraday's skills included being able to devise experiments, to notice patterns and to change his ideas when necessary. He believed in popularising science and began the Royal Institution Christmas Lectures for children that still take place. (They are now televised each year.)

Charles Darwin 1809–1882
English naturalist
Darwin travelled widely and closely observed plant and animal life; he studied similarities and differences between species and developed the theory of evolution. His *The Origin of Species* was published in 1859 and *The Descent of Man* in 1871. He investigated the activity of earthworms and understood their importance in maintaining a fertile soil, describing the earthworm as a miniature plough.

Louis Pasteur 1822-1895
French bacteriologist

Pasteur showed that micro-organisms do not generate spontaneously, as was widely believed, but multiply in air, water and soil. He discovered that 'germs' make beer and wine go sour and that milk can be prevented from turning by heating. Pasteur developed inoculation against anthrax and rabies.

Joseph Lister 1827-1912
English doctor

Using Pasteur's theory that germs in the air cause wounds to become infected, Lister discovered a substance – carbolic acid – that prevents bacteria from multiplying and can be used during operations as an antiseptic.

Marie Curie 1867-1934
Polish scientist who worked in France

Marie Curie searched for radioactivity in materials; she discovered radium and polonium. She persevered with experiments, often under difficult conditions, extracting small amounts of radioactive material from tons of pitchblende residue.

Albert Einstein 1879-1955
German physicist

Einstein developed theories about time, space, light and energy; he explained the discoveries and ideas of other scientists. He realised that motion is relative and nothing travels faster than light. He announced his Theory of Relativity in 1905.

Sir Alexander Fleming 1881-1955 (Scottish doctor).

Sir Alexander Fleming 1881-1955 Scottish doctor

In 1928, Fleming discovered a mould that prevents bacteria from multiplying and does not harm the body's white blood cells. Both serious and common infections are treated today by penicillin. Howard Florey and Ernst Chain developed and purified penicillin; all three men were awarded a Nobel Prize.

Sir Chandrasekhara V Raman 1888-1970 Indian physicist

In 1930 Sir Chandrasekhara won the Nobel Prize for work involving the diffusion of light. He discovered the Raman effect, which is important when investigating molecular structure.

Jocelyn Bell Burnell b.1943 Scottish astronomer

Thirty years ago Jocelyn Bell was involved in the discovery of pulsars (neutron stars), for which her supervisors won the Nobel Prize. She is now Head of Physics at the Open University.

Stephen Hawking b.1942 English cosmologist and physicist

Stephen Hawking's speciality is Black Holes. He is the author of the best-selling book, *A Brief History of Time*. He now works at Cambridge University.

Useful information

A selection of Folens Science resources.

A selection of Folens Science resources

Photopack: Plants
Photopack: Minibeasts
The Picture Bank: Humans
Ideas Bank Science: Materials
and Change
Ideas Bank: Forces
Ideas Bank: Plants and Animals
Ideas Bank: Investigating Life
  Processes and Living Things
Ideas Bank: Investigating
  Materials and their Properties
Ideas Bank: Investigating
  Physical Processes
Flying Start: Science
Key Ideas: Materials
Learning Through Story: Science
Science in Action: Books 1–4

Useful addresses

The Royal Institution of Great Britain
21 Albemarle Street,
London, W1X 4BS
Tel: 0171 409 2992

The Science Museum
Exhibition Road, South
Kensington, London,
SW7 2DD
Tel: 0171 938 8000

The Natural History Museum
Cromwell Road, South
Kensington, London,
SW7 5BD
Tel: 0171 938 9123

The National Museum of Photography, Film and Television
Pictureville, Bradford,
BD1 1NQ
Tel: 01274 727488

Eureka!
Discovery Road, Halifax,
HX1 2NE
Tel: 01422 330069

Snibston Discovery Park
Ashby Road, Coalville,
Leicestershire, LE67 3LN
Tel: 01530 510851

The Exploratory
Bristol Old Station, Temple
Meads, Bristol, BS1 6QU
Tel: 0117 907 5000/907 9000

Organisations that provide advice, books and materials

ASE Association for Science Education
College Lane, Hatfield,
Herts, AL10 9AA
Tel: 01707 267411

LTL Learning Through Landscapes
Third Floor, Southside Offices,
The Law Courts, Winchester,
Hants, SO23 9DL
Tel: 01962 846258

WWF UK
Panda House, Weyside
Park, Godalming, Surrey,
GU7 1XR
Tel: 01483 426444

Cleapse School Science Service
Brunel University, Uxbridge,
UB8 3PH
Tel: 01895 251496

CEE Council for Environmental Education
University of Reading,
Reading, Berks, RG1 5AQ
Tel: 0118 975 6061

The Wildlife Trust
The Green, Witham Park,
Waterside South, Lincoln,
LN5 7JR
Tel: 01522 544400